P9-BBV-886

THIS
BOOK
BELONGS

TO _____

GROLIER
B O O K S

THE PYRAMID CAPER
An Adventure in Egypt

© The Walt Disney Company. All rights reserved.
Printed in the United States of America.
Developed by The Walt Disney Company in conjunction with Nancy Hall, Inc.
ISBN: 0-7172-8318-6
Grolier Books is a division of Grolier Enterprises, Inc.

Huey, Dewey, Louie, Donald and Daisy were leaving the museum, where they had seen the King Tut exhibit.

"I wish we could see the real pyramids," said Huey.

"Yeah!" agreed Dewey. "Going to Egypt would be the trip of a lifetime. But it would probably be expensive."

"Actually," said Daisy, "I saw a sign in the museum about a raffle for a trip for four to Egypt. Why don't we all buy chances and see what happens?"

NATURAL HISTORY MUSEUM

"Great idea!" said all three nephews excitedly.

"Will you buy a ticket too, Uncle Donald?" Louie asked.

"No, thank you," Donald scoffed. "I'd rather not waste my money. Nobody ever wins those raffles."

"Well, somebody must win," replied Daisy. "Let's go back inside and get our tickets, boys!"

A few days later someone from the museum called to say that Daisy had won the trip. It wasn't long before she and the boys had packed their bags and were ready to leave.

Donald tried to be a good sport, even though he felt a little sad at being left behind. "Have a good time," he called out.

But when Donald went back in the house, he felt even lonelier. Just then he spotted the itinerary that Daisy had left for him. "Who needs a dumb raffle to go to Egypt?" he thought. "I'll just get the next flight to Egypt and catch up with them. That would really surprise them!"

Donald quickly packed his bag and raced off to the airport.

Hours later Daisy and the boys landed in Cairo, the biggest city in all of Africa.

"What a busy place!" exclaimed Huey. "There's so much to see."

Dewey looked up at the *minarets*, the thin towers that are part of the domed houses of worship called *mosques*.

Everywhere Daisy and the boys looked they saw a mixture of old and new. Men in business suits walked beside others dressed in long, flowing shirts. In the streets, taxi drivers drove beside carts piled high with vegetables and fruits.

"I wish Donald could see this," said Daisy, snapping a picture of a beautiful mosque.

Their next stop was the Cairo Museum, where they learned about the *pharaohs*, the rulers of ancient Egypt.

"Wow! Look at that!" exclaimed Huey.

"That's a special kind of coffin. Inside is a mummy that is thousands of years old," their guide explained. "The pharaohs and others believed that after people died, they would begin new lives in a different world. In order to preserve their bodies for the next life, they were embalmed and wrapped with cloth bandages."

"Were they put inside the pyramids?" asked Dewey.

"That's right," replied the guide. "They were buried deep inside the pyramids with all the things they would need for the afterlife."

"We're going to see the pyramids tomorrow," Louie told the guide.

"Yes," said Daisy, "but before we do, there's one place I don't want to miss!"

That afternoon Daisy took the boys to the Khalili Bazaar.

"This is amazing!" said Louie.

At each stall people were bargaining in loud voices for the things that were sold there, such as leather goods, food, perfumes, rugs and jewelry.

Huey, Dewey and Louie stopped at one of the tents where a craftsman was selling clay souvenirs. Dewey bought a model of the pyramids, and Huey and Louie bought little statues of the pharaohs.

"I'm glad we found some gifts for Uncle Donald," said Huey. "It's too bad he couldn't join us."

In fact Donald had just arrived—and he was standing in the very next booth! But the market was so crowded that Daisy and the boys didn't see him buying some Egyptian clothing.

The next morning Daisy and the boys went to Giza to
see the pyramids. A tour guide greeted them as they
stepped out of their taxi.

"The best way to get to the pyramids is by camel," he
told them.

"Sounds good to me!" exclaimed Dewey.

"Oh, yes!" said Daisy. "Let's try it!"

The camels got down on their knees so that the
passengers could climb aboard. It wasn't long before the
group was on its way into the desert.

When his camel got to the top of a sand dune, Louie
cried out, "There are the pyramids!" Stretched out before
them were the biggest monuments they had ever seen.

"The pyramids were constructed from individual blocks of stone," explained the guide. "And each block weighed over two tons."

"How did the ancient Egyptians get such heavy stones all the way to the top?" asked Dewey.

"No one really knows for sure," replied the guide. "Since the wheel had not been invented yet, the stones probably had to be dragged up huge dirt ramps with ropes. It sometimes took thousands of people and several lifetimes to build a single pyramid."

Just then, the guide paused as a camel whizzed by them with a shrieking passenger on its back.

"He must be a tourist," said Daisy. "He doesn't seem to know how to handle a camel."

Little did she know that the rider was Donald! A guide rushed off to help him, but by the time Donald returned, Daisy and the boys had already left.

That night, Donald checked Daisy's itinerary again.

"I can't understand why I haven't found them yet," he
said. "Well, I'm sure to catch up with them tomorrow in
Aswan."

But when he tried to fall asleep that night, he worried
about Daisy and his nephews. And the more he thought
about them, the more he tossed and turned.

Donald was so tired when he boarded the plane the next morning that he sat down and fell fast asleep. A little later, Daisy and the boys boarded the same plane, but they didn't recognize Donald in his new clothing.

Poor Donald! He slept through the plane's first stop.

When Daisy and the boys got off at Aswan, Donald stayed asleep in his seat. He didn't wake up until the plane landed at Abu Simbel.

"How did we get here?" sputtered Donald. "I'm supposed to be in Aswan!"

At that very same time, Daisy and the boys were on their way to visit the famous Aswan High Dam.

"The dam is made from many different materials," said their guide. "There is enough sandstone, granite and clay in it to build fifteen pyramids!"

"It sure is big," said Huey, "but what is it for?"

"It is our way of controlling nature," answered the guide. "Before the dam was built, the farmers had problems with too much or too little rain. Now the water flows into the dam, which can store extra water for the dry season. Then the dam brings water to millions of farmers who live in the Nile Valley."

"That's neat," said Huey. The others agreed.

Meanwhile, Donald had decided to make the best of things while he waited for the next plane to Aswan.

He joined a tour group that was on its way to the monuments at Abu Simbel. When the group came to the edge of the Nile River, the guide pointed to several huge figures.

"More than 3,000 years ago, there lived a powerful pharaoh named Ramses II," explained the guide. "He had these statues of himself carved into the sandstone to guard an important temple.

"The temple and statues were originally built in Aswan, but had to be moved here after the Aswan High Dam was built," the guide continued. "Otherwise they would have disappeared beneath the waters of the dam. It took many years to cut them into blocks and move them stone by stone."

"It feels like it's taking me that long to find Daisy and the boys," thought Donald.

Donald caught the next flight to Aswan. As soon as he landed, he hurried over to the docks by the river. He knew that Daisy and the boys were going to Luxor by cruise ship, and he was determined to catch up with them before they boarded.

But once again Donald was just a few minutes too late. He got there just in time to see them sailing away.

"Wait for me!" he shouted. The only one who heard him, though, was a sailor standing next to him.

"Will you help me catch up with my friends?" asked Donald. "They're on that ship."

"Certainly," replied the sailor. "My boat is small but it can go like the wind. I'll try my best."

Donald offered to pay the sailor for his time, and soon they were on their way.

Unfortunately, when they arrived in Luxor, the cruise ship had already pulled in.

Donald thanked the sailor, then found a place to rent a bicycle. As he rode around the city, he looked everywhere for any sign of Daisy and the boys.

Finally he spotted them in the distance. They were getting into a horse-drawn carriage.

"Daisy! Wait up!" Donald cried.

He wasn't going to lose Daisy this time. He would have caught up to her, too, if some flowers hadn't blocked his view.

   Donald took his eyes off the road for an instant to
look at some colorful flowers. Suddenly . . . CRASH! He lay
sprawled in the street with the worried flower dealer
standing over him.
   "You look like you could use a doctor," the dealer said.
"Please let me take you."

The kind man took Donald to a nearby medical office. "Don't worry," said the doctor after he had examined Donald. "You're not as injured as you look. All you have are minor cuts and bruises. These bandages will keep them nice and clean."

Donald thanked the doctor and the flower dealer for their help, and then said good-bye.

Just as he was leaving, Donald saw Daisy and the boys. "Hey!" he called. "Stop!"

"A mummy!" cried Dewey. "And it's coming this way!"

"Huey! Dewey! Louie! It's me, Uncle Donald!" he shouted.

When Daisy and the boys heard Donald's voice, they stopped in their tracks.

"What are you doing here?" cried Daisy, rushing to his side. "What happened to you?"

"I had a little accident," replied Donald. "It looks worse than it is."

"Thank heavens!" cried Daisy, giving him a hug.

"We've been having a great time in Egypt," declared Dewey.

"Yeah, Uncle Donald. It's too bad you missed it," added Huey.

"Oh, I've been all over Egypt," replied Donald. "In fact, it looks like you four are the only things I missed!"

Did You Know...?

There are many different customs and places that make each country special. Do you remember some of the things below from the story?

Cairo is Egypt's capital and the largest city in Africa. Old and new things stand side by side in Cairo. Modern office buildings have been built alongside ancient Moslem temples called *mosques* (MOSKS). Bazaars, or street markets, offer everything from fruits and vegetables to leather goods and camel saddles.

Except for a narrow strip along the Nile river, Egypt is nearly all desert. The desert is extremely hot during the day, but turns very cold when the sun goes down. Only a small part of the desert has sand dunes. Most of it is rocky and hilly. Hope the boys find an oasis soon!

The Nile is the longest river in the world. It runs the length of Africa and provides Egypt with nearly all its water.

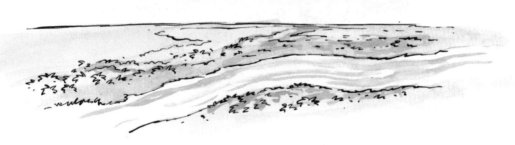

The pyramids were built thousands of years ago as giant tombs for the Egyptian kings, called *pharaohs* (FEHR-ohs). The Great Pyramid of Cheops is made up of over two million stone blocks. Inside the pyramid are many rooms and hidden passageways that once held jewels, statues, and food. Since the pharaohs believed they would begin a new life after death, they wanted all their favorite things with them to use in the afterlife.

The ancient Egyptians created one of the world's first great civilizations. They invented basic arithmetic, a kind of paper made from plants called *papyrus* (pa PIE rus), and a calendar similar to the one we use today.

Hieroglyphic (Hy uhr uh GLIF ik) is a form of picture writing used by the ancient Egyptians. Most of the symbols were pictures of animals, shapes, and other objects. The Egyptians used hieroglyphs to record religious messages and the accomplishments of their pharaohs. They also used them for everyday business transactions.

A minaret is a tall, slender tower on a mosque. Many minarets in Egypt are beautiful works of art. Five times a day a *muezzin* (mu EZ in), or crier, steps out of the minaret's balcony and calls to the people to pray.

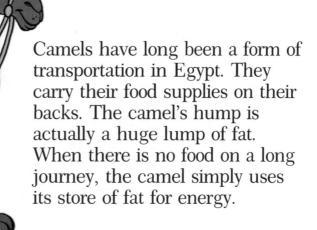

Camels have long been a form of transportation in Egypt. They carry their food supplies on their backs. The camel's hump is actually a huge lump of fat. When there is no food on a long journey, the camel simply uses its store of fat for energy.